The Novello Choral Programme

By *Popular* R

CW00421700

Songs on the lighter side *for mixed voice choirs.*

Selected and edited by Ralph Allwood.

Novello

THE NOVELLO CHORAL PROGRAMME is the creation of a panel
of advisors pre-eminent in the British music scene:
Ralph Allwood, Ann Cartwright, Susan Digby, David Hill, Brian Kay
and Barry Rose, each with extensive experience in choral conducting,
concert work and music education. The aim is to publish essential
editions from the best of the wealth of existing choral music, ancient
and modern, while widening the repertoire with exciting new
composers and new trends in music making.

Cover design by Michael Bell Design.
Music setting by Barnes Music Engraving.

ISBN 0-7119-8546-4
NOV072524

HEAD OFFICE
14-15 Berners Street, London W1T 3LJ, UK.

SALES & HIRE
Music Sales Distribution Centre
Newmarket Road, Bury St Edmunds, Suffolk IP33 3YB, UK.
Telephone: +44 (0)1284 702600
Fax: +44 (0)1284 768301

www.musicsales.com
e-mail: music@musicsales.co.uk

Introduction

The arrangements I have chosen for this collection are all by highly experienced choral musicians who have used similar arrangements in their repertoires for some time, and know what will work. Giving interesting parts to all sections of the choir is one of the challenges of arranging. These pieces are designed to be sung either by small ensembles or by large choirs. Groups should feel free to add percussion parts and be fairly liberal with effects. For example, vocal percussion effects are suggested in *Honey Pie*, but singers should feel free to use others, vetted well in advance, of course, by the conductor! Those who know the original of *Honey Pie* will understand that certain compromises have had to be made for some of the instrumental and vocal effects.

In planning choral programmes it is customary to start with older pieces and get later and later until the 'light' section at the end, after which we can all go home happy. It is worth experimenting with other schemes. For example, audiences which are relatively unfamiliar with sixteenth century music will often breathe a sigh of relief when they hear lighter music at the beginning of the programme, and then listen more attentively to the rest. Or lighter pieces could be inserted throughout the programme. It depends on the audience.

A wide variety of skills is called for in the singing of these songs. *The Way You Look Tonight* needs very careful tuning of the close harmony, and will require much stopping on chords to establish clear intonation. *The Girl from Ipanema* will need several goes through to become familiar with the idiom. *Sit Down, You're Rocking the Boat* needs a 'showbiz' style of performance, perhaps even with some choreography.

It is perhaps worth mentioning the convention of 'swing' for singing or playing pairs of quavers. Essentially, it is something which can only be 'felt' – but the effect is more or less of ♩♪ . In this collection, it is always specified when a certain piece should be 'swung'.

Ralph Allwood. Eton College, October 2000.

The Bare Necessities

Words and music by Terry Gilkyson
Arranged by Nicholas Hare

4

6

want that can't be found. ba   ba

want that can't be found. ba da__ ba da ba   ba

want that can't be found.   If you find out you can live with-out__ it and

bom bom bom bom ba   ba

ba   not think-in' a - bout it, ah_____ ooh_____

ba   not think-in' a - bout it, I'll tell you some-thing true.____

go a-long not think-in' a - bout it,   ba ba ba ba

ba   not think-in' a - bout it,   bom bom bom bom

The bare ne - ces - si - ties, the bare ne - ces - si - ties,

The bare ne - ces - si - ties, the bare ne - ces - si - ties,

ba The bare ne - ces - si - ties, the bare ne -

ba The bare ne - ces - si - ties, the bare ne -

the bare ne - ces - si - ties will come to you._____ yeah!

the bare ne - ces - si - ties will come to you. ba da__ ba da ba yeah!

- ces - si - ties, bare ne - ces - si - ties will come to you. ba da__ ba da ba. yeah!

- ces - si - ties, bare ne - ces - si - ties will come to you._____ yeah!

The Girl from Ipanema

Music by Antonio Carlos Jobim
English words by Norman Gimbel
Arranged by Berty Rice

12

and love - ly The girl from I - pa - ne - ma goes walk - in' And when

Shap sha na na na na da da Shap sha na na na na

Shap sha na na na na da da Shap sha na na na na

Shap sha na na na na da da Shap sha na na na na

__ she pass - es each one__ she pass - es goes 'Ah!'

da da da da sha na na na na da da

da da da da sha na na na na da da

da da da da sha na na na na da da

13

When she walks she's like ___ a sam - ba That swings so cool and sways

da   da   Shap sha na na na na   da   da

da   da   Shap sha na na na na   da   da

da   da   Shap sha na na na na   da   da

___ so gen - tle that when ___ she pass - es each one ___ she pass - es goes 'Ah!'

Shap sha na na na na   da   da   da   da   sha na na na na

Shap sha na na na na   da   da   da   da   sha na na na na

Shap sha na na na na   da   da   da   da   sha na na na na

looks straight a - head not at he.
Tall and tan and young

da da Shap sha na na na na Tall and tan and young

da da Shap sha na na na na Tall and tan and young

da da Shap sha na na na na Tall and tan and young

_ and love - ly The girl from I - pa - ne - ma goes walk-in' And when_ she pass - es He smiles,

_ and love - ly The girl from I - pa - ne - ma goes walk-in' And when_ she pass - es He smiles,

_ and love - ly The girl from I - pa - ne - ma goes walk-in' And when_ she pass - es He smiles,

_ and love - ly The girl from I - pa - ne - ma goes walk-in' And when_ she pass - es He smiles,

but she does-n't see.___ She just does-n't see._

Shap sha na na na na da da

Shap sha na na na na da da

Shap sha na na na na da da

Da da da da da da da da___

Shap sha na na na na Tall and tan and young and love - ly The

Shap sha na na na na da da Shap sha na na na na

Shap sha na na na na da da Shap sha na na na na

18

20

Oh,_____ but he wat-ches so sad - ly.___

sha na na na na da da da sha na na na na

_ but he wat-ches so sad - ly___

da da sha na na na na da da

_ How_____ can he tell her he loves her?___

da da da sha na na na na da da da sha na na na na

How_____ can he tell her he loves her?___

sha na na na na da da sha na na na na da da

Yes,_____ he would give his heart

da da da sha na na na na da da da

Yes,_____ he would give his heart glad - ly_____

sha na na na na da da sha na na na na

glad - ly___ But each day when she walks to the sea She

sha na na na na da da Shap sha na na na na

But each day when she walks to the sea She

da da da da Shap sha na na na na

looks straight a - head not at he. Tall and tan and young

da da Shap sha na na na na Tall and tan and young

looks straight a - head not at he. Tall and tan and young

da da Shap sha na na na na Tall and tan and young

_ and love - ly The girl from I - pa - ne - ma goes walk-in' And when_ she pass-es He smiles,

_ and love - ly The girl from I - pa - ne - ma goes walk-in' And when_ she pass-es He smiles,

_ and love - ly The girl from I - pa - ne - ma goes walk-in' And when_ she pass-es He smiles,

_ and love - ly The girl from I - pa - ne - ma goes walk-in' And when_ she pass-es He smiles,

24

Goodnight Sweetheart

Words and music by Calvin Carter and James Hudson
Arranged by Kirby Shaw

time to go,__ I hate to leave you, but I real-ly must say,__ Good-

time to go,__ I hate to leave you, but I real-ly must say,__ Good-

time to go,__ I hate to leave you, but I real-ly must say,__ Good-

do___ do do, do do do do___ do do___ do do, Good-

- night sweet-heart, Good-night.__ Well it's

- night sweet-heart, Good-night.__ __ good - night, Well

- night sweet-heart, Good-night.__ __ good - night, Well

- night sweet - heart, Good - night.__ Do do dn do ___ good-night, Well

26

three o - clock___ in the morn-ing,_ and___ ba - by__ I just can't get

du du du_ du du du du du du___ du du du du

du du du_ du du du du du du___ du du du du

du___ du du du du du du___ du du du du du du du du du du du

right,_____ Well,_ I hate to leave you ba - by,___ I

du,_____ du du du du du du du

du,_____ du du du du du dn du du du du du dn du

don't mean may - be,___ be - cause I love___ you so.___

du du du_____ be - cause I love you so.___

du du du_____ be - cause I love you so.___

du du du_____ be - cause I love you so.___ Do do dn do do dn do do dn do

TUTTI

Good-night sweet-heart, well___ it's time to go,___

Good-night sweet-heart, well___ it's time to go,___

Good-night sweet-heart, well___ it's time to go,___

do_____ do do_____ do do_____ do do do do dn do

mo-ther_ and your fa-ther_ might not like it___ if I stay here_ too_

Du du wop, du du wop, du du wop, du du wop, du du wop, du du wop,

Du du wop, du du wop, du du wop, du du wop, du du wop, du du wop,

Du du wop, du du wop, du du wop, du du wop, du du wop, du du wop,

long.___ Well, I hate to_ leave you ba - by,_ I don't mean may-be_ you

wo wo wo wo___ du du wop, du du wop, I don't mean may - be_ you

wo wo wo wo___ du du wop, du du wop, I don't mean may - be_ you

wo wo wo wo___ du du wop, du du wop, I don't mean may - be, Don't you

know I love you so. Good-night sweet-heart, well it's

know I love you so. Good-night sweet-heart, well it's

know I love you so. Good-night sweet-heart, well it's

know I love you so. Do do dn do do dn do do dn do do do do do

time to go, Good-night sweet-heart, well it's time to go,

time to go, Good-night sweet-heart, well it's time to go,

time to go, Good-night sweet-heart, well it's time to go,

do do do, do do dn do do do do do do do do, do do do

I hate to leave you, but I real-ly must say,— Good-night sweet-heart, Good - night.

I hate to leave you, but I real-ly must say,— Good-night sweet-heart, Good - night.

I hate to leave you, but I real-ly must say,— Good-night sweet-heart, Good - night.

do_____ do do_____ do_ do do do Good-night sweet - heart, Good - night.

— Good - night,_____ sweet-heart good - night._____

— Good - night,_____ Good-night, sweet-heart good - night._____

— Good - night,_____ sweet-heart good-night, sweet-heart good-night.

— Good - night,_____ sweet-heart good - night._____ (Solo) Good-night.

Here, There and Everywhere

Words and music by John Lennon and Paul McCartney
Arranged by Berty Rice

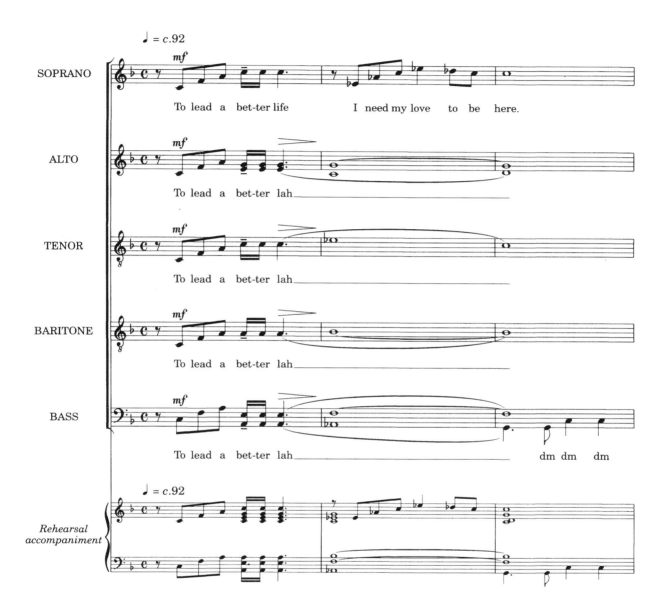

34

Know-ing that love__ is to share__ each one be - liev - ing that love_

ne - ver dies__ watch-ing her eyes__ and hop-ing I'm al - ways there.

39

Honey Pie

Words and music by John Lennon and Paul McCartney
Arranged by Martin Pickard

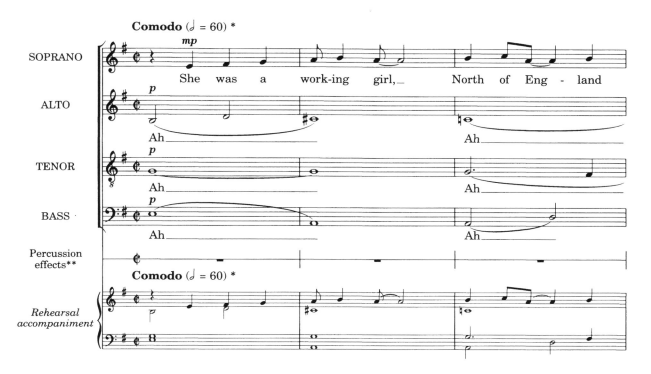

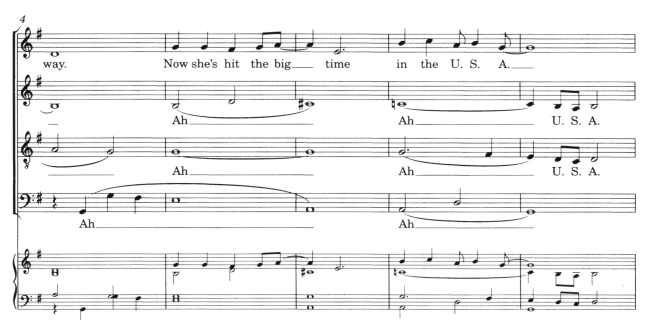

* The quaver rhythms should be 'swung' throughout.

** The percussion effects should be performed by one or more of the singers themselves, either orally or with instruments. Sounds suggested here are only a guide.

* The SOLO and TUTTI indications in the Tenor part are optional in performances by choirs.

44

45

I'm Beginning to See the Light

*Words and music by Harry James, Duke Ellington,
Johnny Hodges and Don George
Arranged by Berty Rice*

then you came_____ that's a four a-larm fi - re*__
then you came_____ that's a four a-larm fi - re*__
then you came_____ that's a four a-larm fi - re*__
in the dark, Then you came and caused a spark, That's a four a-larm fi-re* now.

[*'fa-yer']

S & A

now._____ I ne-ver made love by lan-tern shine, I ne-ver saw rain-bows
now._____
T & B
I ne-ver made love by lan-tern shine, I ne-ver saw rain-bows

in my wine, But now that your lips are burn-ing mine, I'm be - gin-ning to see the light.
in my wine, But now that your lips are burn-ing mine, I'm be - gin-ning to see the light.

54

seen the light.   I   have   seen the light,   I'm be - gin-ning   to

seen the light.   I   have   seen the light,   I'm be - gin-ning   to

seen the light.   I   have   seen the light,   I'm be - gin-ning   to

seen the light.   I   have   seen the light,   I'm be - gin-ning   to

see   the   light._____

see   the   light._____

see   the   light._____

see   the   light._____

Is You Is Or Is You Ain't My Baby?

Words and music by Billy Austin and Louis Jordan
Arranged by James Oxley

D.S. al Coda

Lullaby of Birdland

Words by George David Weiss
Music by George Shearing
Arranged by Alexander L'Estrange

how I feel. Have you e - ver heard two tur - tle doves

doo doot Have you e - ver heard two tur - tle doves

doo doot Have you e - ver heard two tur - tle doves

doo doot Oh have you e - ver, e - ver heard two tur - tle doves, you hear them

bill and coo___ when_ they love? That's the kind of mag - ic

bill and coo___ when_ they love? That's the kind of mag - ic

bill and coo___ when_ they love? That's the kind of mag - ic

bill and coo___ when_ they love, oh That's the kind of mag - ic

doo (boo hoo hoo hoo)_____ If_____

doo (boo hoo hoo hoo)_____ If_____

cry, That's how I'd cry in my pil-low, If_____

dm - ba dm dm dm dm dm dm (my pil-low) if_____

_____ you should tell me fare-well_____ and good-bye. Ah, Lul-la-by of Bird-land,

_____ you should tell me fare-well_____ and good-bye. Ah, Lul-la-by of Bird-land,

_____ you should tell me fare-well_____ and good-bye. Ah, Lul-la-by of Bird-land,

_____ you should tell me fare-well,_____ good-bye. Ah, Lul-la-by of Bird-land,

whis - per low, ___ kiss me sweet, and ___ we'll go ___ fly - in' high,

whis - per low, ___ kiss me sweet, and ___ we'll go ___ fly -

whis - per low, ___ kiss me sweet, and ___ we'll go ___ fly -

whis - per low, whis-per and kiss me sweet, and ___ we'll go ___ fly -

___ way up in Bird-land, high ___ in the sky ___ up a-bove, ___ all be - cause

- in' high in Bird-land, high ___ in the sky ___ up a-bove, ___ doo ___ doo doo ___

- in' high in Bird-land, high ___ in the sky ___ up a-bove, ___ doo ___ doo doo ___

- in' high in Bird-land, high ___ in the sky ___ up a-bove ___ all be - cause doo doo ___

74

doo ba doo d'n doot doot doot doot doo ba doo dap

doo ba doo d'n doot doot doot doot doo ba doo dap

doo ba doo d'n doot doot doot doot doot doo dap

- doo ba doo d'n doot doot doot doot doot doo dap ba dm dm dm

ba ooh_____ doot

ba ooh_____ doot

Ba doo - ba dwee - ba doo - d'n - da doo (how's your fa - ther)

doo ba doo - dap ba dm dm dm dm dm dm dm dm

78

Lul - la - by of Bird - land, whis - per low,— kiss me sweet,

Lul - la - by of Bird - land, whis - per low,— kiss me sweet,

Lul - la - by of Bird - land, whis - per low,— kiss me sweet,

Lul - la - by of Bird - land, whis - per low,— whis-per and kiss me sweet,

and— we'll go— fly - in' high,— way up in Bird-land, high— in the sky— up a-bove,—

and— we'll go— fly - in' high in Bird-land, high— in the sky— up a-bove,—

and— we'll go— fly - in' high in Bird-land, high— in the sky— up a-bove,—

and— we'll go— fly - in' high in Bird-land, high— in the sky— up a-bove,—

Miss Otis Regrets

Words and music by Cole Porter
Arranged by Martin Pickard

If performed by a choir, Soprano 1 in verse 1 and Tenor 1 in verse 2 may be sung by solo voices.

Satin Doll

Words by Johnny Mercer
Music by Duke Ellington and Billy Strayhorn
Arranged by Berty Rice

youre flip-pin'— speaks La-tin— that— Sa-tin Doll.

youre flip-pin'— speaks La-tin— that— Sa-tin Doll.

youre flip-pin'— speaks La-tin— that— Sa-tin Doll.

doo be doo-wah— be doo be dm dm dm dm doo be doo wah— be doot

ooh_____

ooh_____

ooh_____

door v dm dm dm dm dm dm She's no-bo-dy's fool, so I'm play-ing it cool as can be,—

97

for Nigel Perrin and Bath Camerata

Sit Down, You're Rockin' the Boat

Words and music by Frank Loesser
Arranged by Grayston Ives

The Way You Look Tonight

Words by Dorothy Fields
Music by Jerome Kern
Arranged by John Rutter

Where Do I Begin?

(Theme from *Love Story*)
Words by Carl Sigman
Music by Francis Lai
Arranged by Adrian Lucas

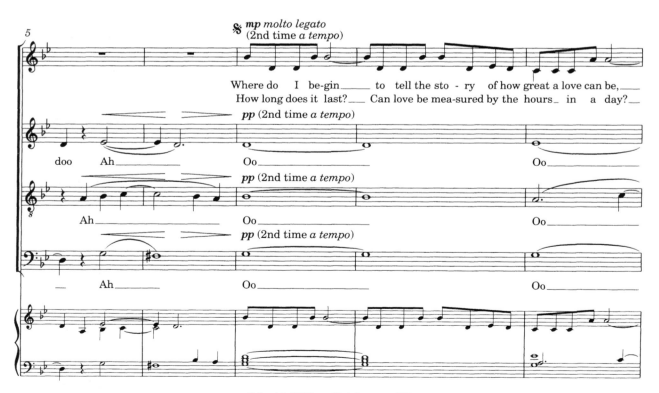

she gave a mean-ing to this emp-ty world of mine:_____ There'd ne-ver be a-no-ther

doo doo doo. Doo doo doo doo doo doo doo.

__ doo doo____ doo doo. Doo doo____ doo doo____ doo doo____ doo doo.

Doo doo doo doo.__ Doo doo doo. Doo doo doo doo.__

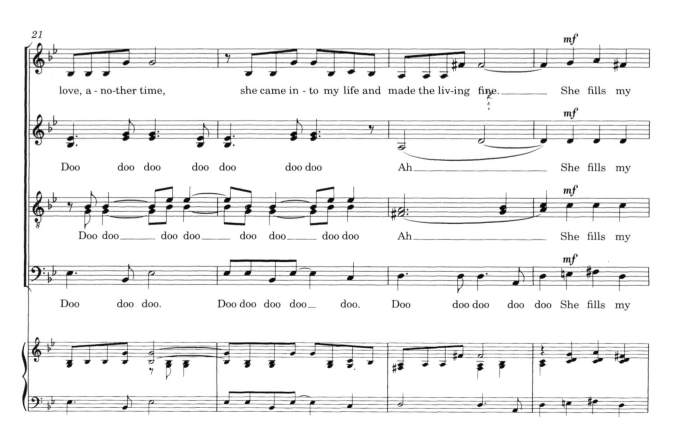

love, a-no-ther time, she came in-to my life and made the liv-ing fine._____ She fills my

Doo doo doo doo doo doo doo Ah_____ She fills my

Doo doo____ doo doo____ doo doo____ doo doo Ah_____ She fills my

Doo doo doo. Doo doo doo doo__ doo. Doo doo doo doo doo She fills my

heart, She fills my heart Ah

heart She fills my heart Ah Ah

heart She fills my heart with ve-ry spe-cial things, with an-gel songs, with wild i -

heart She fills my heart Ba dum ba dum ba dum Dum ba dum ba

— Ah I'm ne-ver

Ah Ah

- ma-gin-ings. She fills my soul with so much love that ev-'ry where I go Ah

dum ba dum. Dum ba dum. Ah ba dum ba

01/17 (199661)